KU-428-876

Where is the Bear?

Words by Camilla de la Bédoyère

Illustrations by Emma Levey

MiLeS KELLY

Hi **Suki**! We have a birthday present for our cousin Ping, but we can't find him.

Can you help us?

First published in 2016 by Miles Kelly Publishing Ltd
Harding's Barn, Bardfield End Green, Thaxted, Essex, CM6 3PX, UK

Copyright © Miles Kelly Publishing Ltd 2016

This edition published in 2018

2 4 6 8 10 9 7 5 3 1

Publishing Director Belinda Gallagher
Creative Director Jo Cowan
Editorial Director Rosie Neave
Design Manager Simon Lee
Production Elizabeth Collins, Caroline Kelly
Reprographics Stephan Davis, Jennifer Cozens
Assets Lorraine King

All rights reserved. No part of this publication may be reproduced, stored in a retrieval system, or transmitted by any means, electronic, mechanical, photocopying, recording or otherwise, without the prior permission of the copyright holder.

ISBN 978-1-78617-447-5

Printed in China

British Library Cataloguing-in-Publication Data
A catalogue record for this book is available from the British Library

Made with paper from a sustainable forest

www.mileskelly.net

We have bears here in the Californian **redwood forest**, Suki, but I've never met a bear called Ping.

If you're not Ping, who are you?

I'm an **American black bear**. I'm tearing bark off this tree so I can find juicy bugs hiding underneath!

If you match the animals to their descriptions you will reach an owl who may be able to help. I'm a **yellow-cheeked chipmunk**. I climb trees to find insects, seeds, leaves, nuts and flowers to eat. I live in a cosy burrow at the foot of this tree.

I'm striped to warn that I can sting.
My busy buzz is how I sing.
What am I?

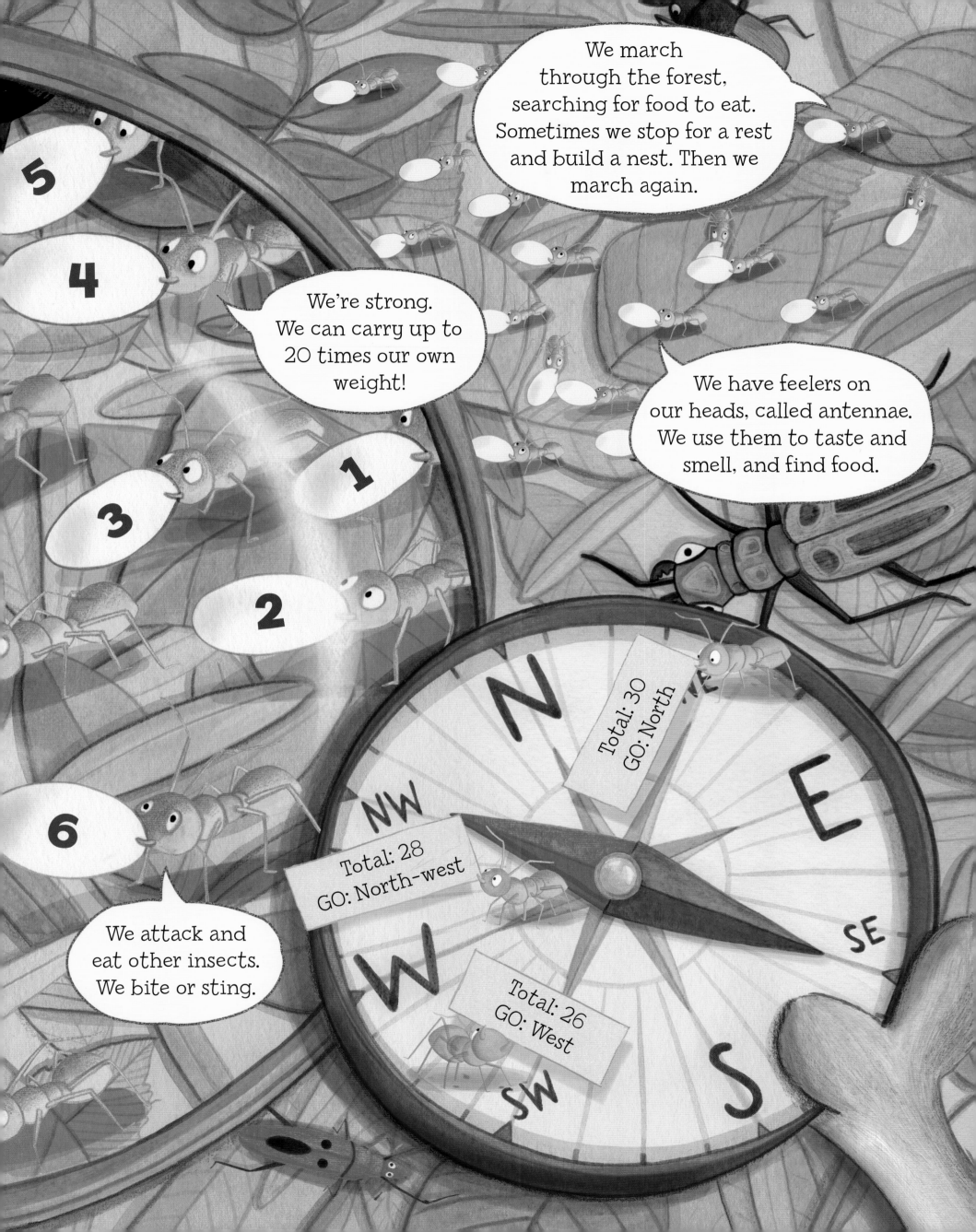

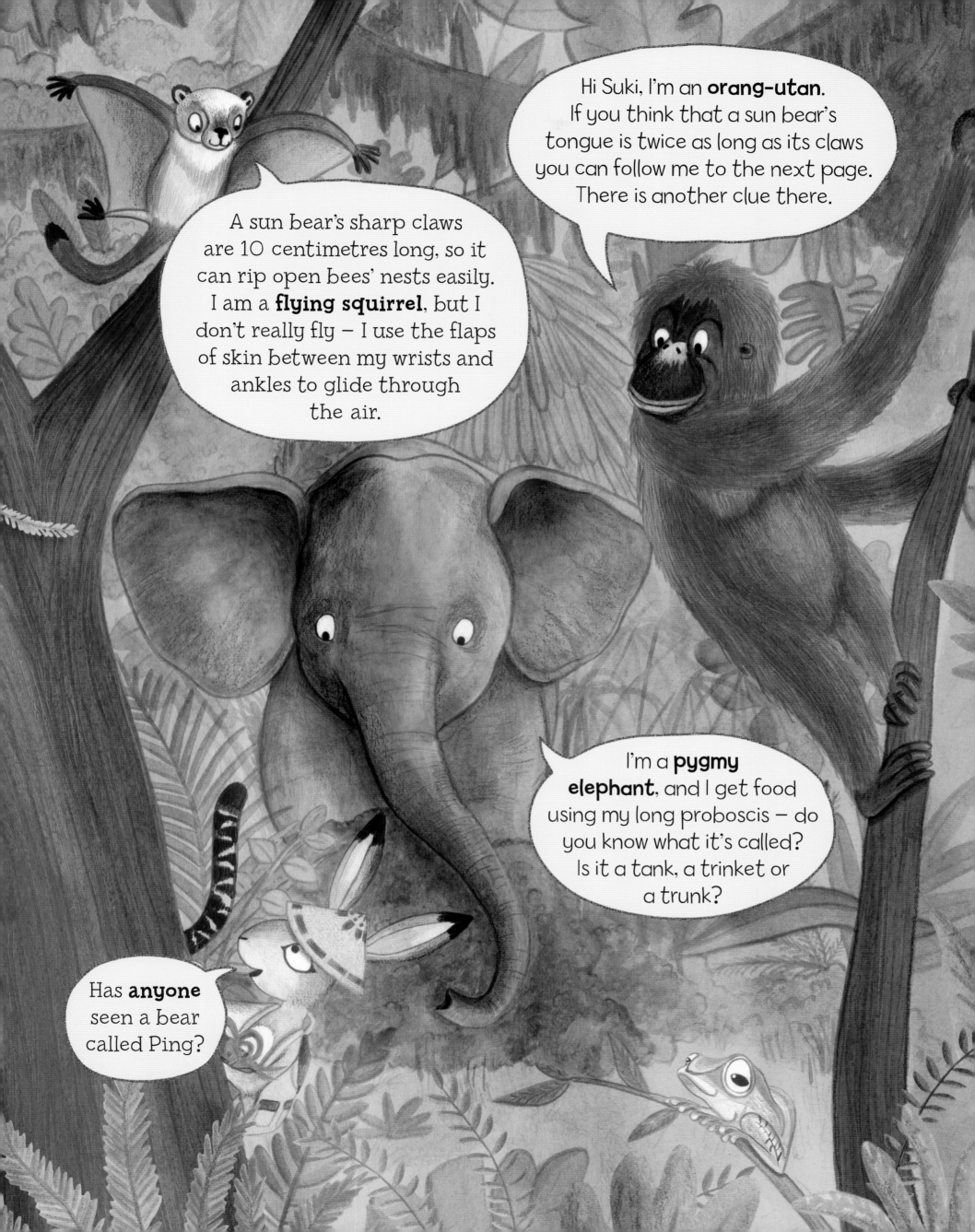

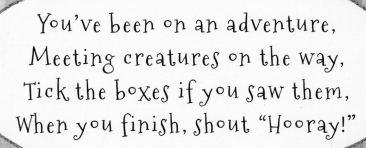

How did your spotting skills shape up?

You've been on an adventure,
Meeting creatures on the way,
Tick the boxes if you saw them,
When you finish, shout "Hooray!"

Rajah Brook's birdwing butterfly

Buzzard

Yellow-throated marten

Spangled drongo

Steller's jay

Walrus

Golden pheasant

Ermine

Borneo eared frog

Chamois

Mistletoe bird

Lace monitor

White-tailed eagle

Green-capped tanager

Mountain goat

Dark green fritillary butterfly

Arctic skua

King cobra

Glass frog

Ural owl

Spiny rat

Bornean bristlehead

Reindeer

Andean cock-of-the-rock

Ivory gull

Greater glider

Horned curassow

Clouded leopard

Sugar glider

Monitor lizard

Roe deer

Graceful tree frog

Geoffroy's cat

Arctic wolf

Northern spotted owl

Spotted nutcracker